Life and Times in Shoe City:
The Shoe Workers of Lynn

text by Keith Melder, Guest Curator

A special exhibition at the Essex Institute
September 14, 1979 - January 27, 1980

Essex Institute, Salem, Massachusetts, 1979

Acknowledgments

The implementation of an exhibition and its programs requires the skills and talents of many different people and to the following we are very appreciative: Martin Blatt, Cynthia Cetlin, Marcia Ciro, Professor John J. Fox and his Salem State College Oral History class, Pamela Guren, Susan Edwards, Emily Hiestand, Gary Kincaid, Dean Lahikainen, Randolph Langenbach, Keith Melder, Allen Moore, Jr., Ed Moreno, Bettina Norton, Naomi L. Rosenblum, Mark Sipson, Kenneth Turino, Ann Wallace, John Wright and other staff members at the Essex Institute who have been helpful. In addition the Essex Institute owes a debt of gratitude to all those individuals and institutions who have provided information, artifacts, documents and support for ''Life and Times in Shoe City: The Shoe Workers of Lynn,'' it is their exhibition: Hersh Adelstein, American Hellenic Protective Association, Ancient Order of Hibernians, Wayne Anderson and his Northeastern University Oral History class, Peter Bates, Bath Marine Museum, Mary H. Blewett, Fred Bloom, Paul Bonnevie, Elaine Bonney, Boston Public Library, Print Dept., Benjamin Bronstein, Mr. and Mrs. Frederick H. Bubier, Building Dept., City of Lynn, Mary Lou Cahalane, William Cashman, Joseph Castaldo, Central Congregational Church, Lynn, Charles Collazzo, Gertrude Connolly, Harry Coppola, Brian Corriveau, William Costley, John Cumbler, Robert D'Atillio, Mrs. Maurice Darling, Alan Dawley, Gary Dickson, John Donahue, Paul Faler, Vincent Ferrini, The First Church of Christ in Lynn, Congregational, Footwear Division, Amalgamated Clothing and Textile Workers Union, Footwear Division, United Food and Commercial Workers International Union, Vicki Frozeloni, Father John Gallagher, Natalie Gallagher, Nathan Gass, Chick Gecoya, Angelo Georgian, Eleanor Gifford, Grand Army of the Republic, Post 5, Lynn, Jim Green, Al Hamilton, John Hardy, Hudson Shoe Machinery, Co., International Union of Electrical Workers—Local 201, Milton Isenberg, Morton Jacobs, Arthur Kaledin, Philip Kaplan, Bruce Kupelnick, Donnal Landry, Library of Congress, Division of Prints and Photographs, Lynn City Hall, Lynn Historical Society, Lynn Public Library, Lynn Yacht Club, Edward L. Madow, Faith Magoun, Gerald Maranucci, Robert Marcotte, Antonio Marino, Lester Matthews, Ed Matvichuck, Eli Mavros, John Mavros, Philip McLella, Vincent McManus, Stella Morris, Jack Musinsky, National Museum of History and Technology, Smithsonian Institution, The New-York Historical Society, Grace Nomey, Oscar Papanastasiou, George Pappas, Robert Paras, Tony Pavone, the Misses Rando, Susan Reverby, Frederick S. Reynolds, Jr., Gary Robinson, James F. Robinson, Larry Rosenblatt, St. Jean's Credit Union, St. Jean Baptiste Church, St. Joseph's Church, St. Michael's Church, St. Stephen's Church, all in Lynn, John Scanlon, William N. Scanlon, Richard Shafner, Barbara Shaler, Joseph Shanahan, Henrietta Sitkowski, Jennie Stankiewicz, Anita Stockbridge, the Rev. Arvel Steece, Arnold Trachtman, Mrs. John Trickey, Phyllis Tsagaris, United Shoe Machinery Corp., Harold Walker, William L. Warren, James Weeks, Cecil Weinstein, George Worth, Dorothy Yeaton, May Young, Clara Zamejtis. The Lynn residents who participated in the ''Old Photos of Lynn'' contest and the oral history programs are too numerous to mention individually, but their interest and resources have provided valuable background for the exhibition. As we go to press we hope more Lynners will come forth with aid to our project, for it is after all in many senses *their* project.

Anne Farnam
Curator

Bryant F. Tolles, Jr.
Director and Librarian

© Copyright 1979 by the Essex Institute
Salem, Massachusetts 01970
All Rights Reserved
Library of Congress Cataloging and Publication Data
ISBN 0-88389-101-8
Designed by Hiestand Design Associates
Typesetting by Eastern Composition Inc.
Printed at Naiman Press
Photographs by Randolph Langenbach
The exhibition and its publications have been generously supported
by a grant from the National Endowment for the Humanities, a federal
agency.

Preface

The recovery of the spiritual and physical evidence of a late nineteenth-century industrial community such as Lynn for a museum exhibition has broad implications for understanding our twentieth-century New England lives. Industrialization radically changed the landscape of New England during the nineteenth-century, and Essex County was no exception. Yet today that once established economic base in the manufacture of such basic goods as shoes and textiles has largely fled the region, first to the American south and west and later to Europe and the Far East. What has happened to New England communities in this process of change? How have local residents adjusted to new forces in the economy and what has happened to urban environments built to serve a single purpose—in Lynn's case for the manufacture of shoes? How can an industrial community become aware of the importance of its past in order to better reshape its future? How does it recover the richness and complexity of its social history—the lives of its people, their beliefs, their customs?

By gathering together the artifacts, documents, memorabilia and photographs of Lynn and her people for our exhibition, ''Life and Times in Shoe City: The Shoe Workers of Lynn,'' we hope to suggest the community's rich and diverse past. In publishing our catalogs and walking tour and offering a variety of public programs in connection with the exhibition, we plan to actively explore some of the themes of that past. The enthusiastic support of many people in Lynn, the dedication of our Institute staff, guest scholars and consultants, and the generosity of the National Endowment for the Humanities have made this project possible, and to all individuals we express appreciation. An exhibition of this sort is a community endeavor, and its success depends upon the lively spirit of those participating. Over the past two years of working on this project we have all enjoyed encountering that spirit in the city of Lynn.

Anne Farnam
Bryant F. Tolles, Jr.

The story told in the exhibition, "Life and Times in Shoe City: The Shoe Workers of Lynn," is a history of change brought about by people—change which transformed their lives. At first we confront industrial change in Lynn: people in the shoe business gradually, then more rapidly, altered their craft and the whole organization of shoe production. In the second half of the nineteenth century, a traditional handicraft became a minutely subdivided series of processes largely done by machines.

Change did not end with mechanization. The community of Lynn changed in fundamental ways, growing from a dispersed rural town into a congested city. The population expanded and became highly diverse with the addition of thousands of non-English-speaking shoe workers. Social life was greatly complicated, with the establishment of hundreds of formal organizations and informal groups. Disparities of wealth and class increased. A vigorous labor movement contended with shoe company management over wages and working conditions. Finally, changing industrial patterns in the second and third quarters of the twentieth century ended the reign of Shoe City. By 1975 shoe manufacturing had nearly vanished from Lynn. Through the years people promoted change, unaware of its consequences; the sequence of developments was largely unforeseen.

Change grew out of the shoe industry in Lynn. It began in the mid-eighteenth century when the city became a center for the making of women's shoes. John Adam Dagyr, an immigrant shoemaker from Wales, taught Lynn workers techniques for improving their craft: how to divide their work more efficiently, and how to produce more fashionable and attractive footwear. The improvements fostered by Dagyr increased the market for Lynn shoes and promoted the steady expansion of the town's population of craftspeople.

In the late eighteenth and early nineteenth centuries shoemaking was strictly a handicraft task. Using traditional tools and ancient mehtods, working out of their homes, men made whole shoes. In Lynn, women also worked in the craft as binders, assembling and stitching together shoe uppers. Their handiwork fit easily into household routines, making women an integral part of Lynn's shoe industry.

One of the first memorable changes came in the late eighteenth century when pressure of business caused men to move shoe benches out of their homes into small separate shoe shops, known as "ten-footers," in reference to their size. In these shops, which became trademarks of the Lynn shoe craft, there congregated the shop owner or master, one or more journeymen shoemakers, and frequently a boy or two — apprentices learning the trade. Such miniature shops, now remembered fondly, were Lynn's original shoe "factories." Hours were long, pay was low, but life was not so difficult. Workers largely controlled the conditions of labor and the pace of work. Discipline tended to be quite relaxed, conviviality and comaraderie generally reigned. Such circumstances survived for about two to three generations, giving Lynn's craftsmen a tradition of independence and individualism.

Between 1820 and 1850 some of the more prominent bosses or shop owners set out to "reform" the shoe manufacturing process, reducing the independence of craftsmen. With accumulated capital and better access to markets, these early entrepreneurs constructed central shops in which they managed the cutting of leather and exerted quality control over their products. Shoe binding and assembly remained decentralized, however. Slowly, through the 1830s and '40s, the size and influence of these central shops grew. By 1850 they were poised for another great change.

Meanwhile, to counteract the increasing power held by bosses, shoemakers and binders organized. A journeyman cordwainers' organization appeared for men as early as 1830. Late in 1833 women shoe binders banded together to form the Female Society of Lynn and Vicinity for the Protection and Promotion of Female Industry. These early labor bodies began the pattern of a vigorous, assertive labor movement in Lynn. They aimed to keep wages up, to exert the workers' influence over the pace and conditions of work, and otherwise to improve the social and economic lives of their members. Organized labor was one manifestation of a strenuous radicalism in the town, encompassing immediate abolitionism, religious diversity, temperance, political egalitarianism, and socialism. In 1844 and 1845, a revived labor movement published its own newspaper, the weekly *Awl*.

During the 1850s and '60s shoe manufacturing experienced the profound impact of mechanization. Machines, factories, and industrial regimentation replaced hand-work, small shops, and informality. One of the early crucial machines, an adaptation of the sewing machine, replaced hand stitching in the making of shoe uppers. Introduced in Lynn in 1852, stitching machines gradually removed the domestic work of shoe binders from the home to the factory. Another device, the McKay stitcher, was first used in Lynn in 1862. It helped to mechanize the stitching of shoe soles to uppers. Many different machines eliminated hand-work in cutting, trimming, and shaping leather. One of these, the skiving machine, was designed to bevel the edges of leather pieces so they could be folded and fitted together. Finally, in the 1880s, one of the most complex processes of all, the lasting of shoes, was adapted to performance by a machine — the hand-method lasting machine. Every machine increased productivity, added to the minute division of labor in the industry, and reduced workers' skills and independence.

Between 1860 and 1900 Lynn was an important center for the invention and manufacture of shoe machinery. Among the many Lynn inventors who contributed materially to revolutionizing the industry, two individuals stood out. One of the most prolific innovators was Seth D. Tripp (1825-1898) whose first contrivance, a pegging machine, was followed by many others, including a counter skiver, rolling machine, shank cutter, and many more. Tripp formed a machinery company in Lynn to produce his most famous invention, the Tripp Giant Leveller. Lynn's most romantic story surrounding an inventor of shoe machinery concerns Jan Earnst Matzeliger (1852-1889). An immigrant from the Dutch West Indies, of Dutch and African ancestry, Matzeliger came to Lynn in 1877, entered employment in a shoe factory, and soon began to tinker at mechanizing the task that many persons believed could not be done by machines — lasting. After three years of work in his spare time, he completed the primitive model of a device which approximated the working of a man's hand. Another model and three more years of work enabled Matzeliger to secure patent number 274,207 for his lasting machine in March 1883. All this time he had lived under conditions of extreme hardship, devoting all his resources to the invention. After being proven in factory tests in 1885, the lasting machine went into production. But the inventor did not live to enjoy his reward: he fell victim to tuberculosis in 1889 at the age of 37. He is remembered as one of our greatest Afro-American inventors.

Important late nineteenth-century machine companies in Lynn included the Tripp Giant Leveller Company, the Bresnahan Shoe Machinery Company, the Boston Machine Works, and others.

Changing industrial conditions — mechanization, the growth of factories, and a prolonged depression — brought a vigorous reaction from the workers. Building on their earlier radical tradition, the shoe workers of Lynn staged a massive strike in 1860. Although it originated in Natick, the largest body of strikers from a single place came from Lynn. Beginning on George Washington's birthday, the great strike lasted about eight weeks and engaged 4,000 or more Lynn workers. Among the spirited events of the strike were numerous demonstrations, five grand processions through the city's streets, countless meetings, chowder parties and other festivities. Men and women shared their stand against oppression; more than a third of the walkout's participants were women. In the end the strikers largely failed in their attempt to raise wages and gain a voice in governing shop conditions. But they had organized the most sizable single strike in pre-Civil War America.

Industrialization changed Lynn physically from a rural town into a congested city. In the ten-footer era, manufacturing had been dispersed in many of Lynn's neighborhoods. Boston Street in West Lynn, the Common and vicinity, Market Street, Broad and Lewis Streets were all prime locations for small shoe shops. Probably the most intense concentration of shoemaking in the preindustrial period existed in the section called Woodend near the intersections of Essex, Chestnut, and Fayette Streets. The opening of the Eastern Railroad (later Boston and Maine) through Central Square in 1838 encouraged the city to grow near the station there. By the 1870s a dense commercial and manufacturing district had developed on streets radiating from the railroad at Central Square. This is clearly shown in an 1879 lithograph of the ''Manufacturing Center of Lynn, Mass.''

Shoe factories soon surpassed the old central shops in size, growing to accommodate hundreds of employees and banks of steam-powered machinery. The great fire of 1889 consumed much of central Lynn but the city was quickly rebuilt. Older, less-massive factories lost to the flames were replaced by large brick blocks constructed for rental to tenant manufacturers. This trend climaxed with the huge Vamp Building, constructed in 1903 and enlarged in 1907. For many years this massive brick pile, occupying nearly a full city block, was the largest shoe factory structure in the world. Lynn's final new shoe plant, the A. M. Creighton factory, was completed about 1924. Many of the factory buildings still remain in Lynn, some of them partially occupied, others nearly empty, as silent reminders of the city's glory years.

The industrial revolution in shoemaking produced a distinct class of entrepreneurs and manufacturers with affluent lifestyles. Two nineteenth-century industrial and civic leaders exemplify such men. Samuel Mansfield Bubier (1816-1894), represented in the ''Shoe City'' exhibition by photographs and several artifacts, learned the shoemaking trade from his father in the latter's small ten-footer shoe shop. Bubier became Lynn's most productive shoe manufacturer, its fifteenth mayor in 1878 and 1879, and an important real estate developer. Philip Augustus Chase (1834-1903), like Bubier a native of Lynn, entered shoe manufacturing in the 1850s, became a pioneer of mechanization, retired from the shoe industry after twenty-six years, then served as president of the Central National Bank and the Lynn Institution for Savings. He helped to found several major city institutions.

In keeping with their spirit of enterprise and their affluence, the manufacturers established varied prominent social institutions. Churches such as St. Stephen's Episcopal, Central Congregational, and the Unitarian Church offered architectural and spiritual reassurance. The Lynn Yacht, Park, and Oxford Clubs provided places to gather, congenial company, and leisure-time activities. When the Oxford Club opened its new clubhouse in 1892, an attractive bazaar was held to celebrate. The bazaar included "a display of boots and shoes of all grades, goat, kid and morocco stock, leather and cut soles, thread, shoe findings and everything but machinery that is used in producing a shoe." Thus did social and industrial pursuits intersect. When Lynn's old families of shoe manufacturers founded the Lynn Historical Society in 1897, one of their early efforts was to collect and equip a small shoe shop of the ten-footer era to commemorate "the style of structure from which the great shoe industry of the United States took its start." The Historical Society often met in the Oxford Clubhouse and elected as its first president Philip Augustus Chase.

With the growth in prosperity of a small group of manufacturers and the concentration of thousands of workers, Lynn became a city of contrasts. The differences in lifestyle between industrialists and workers are displayed in the Essex Institute exhibition through two furniture bills, one for refurnishing Samuel Bubier's house in 1869, the other for furnishing the apartment of the Weinstein family, recent immigrants from England, in 1914.

As the shoe industry grew, so did Lynn's labor movement. In the late 1860s and early '70s, the Knights and Daughters of St. Crispin conducted vigorous organizing activities and labor stoppages among the shoe workers. But resistance from management and the depression in 1873 halted its work. Again in the 1880s, another union, the Knights of Labor, flourished in Lynn, but failed to develop a strong permanent influence. By the 1890s, several different unions were competing for workers' loyalty and support. For example, the Lasters' Protective Union attempted to influence wages and working conditions in one of the most skilled shoe operations. The introduction of lasting machinery was a bitter blow to this union. About 1895 the Boot and Shoe Workers Union was organized and gained a strong following in Lynn.

By the early twentieth century Lynn had the reputation of being a "chaotic" labor union center. It was this "chaos" that the Boot and Shoe Workers Union set out to resolve. The new organization's major weapon was the union stamp — a label attached to all shoes made under contracts between management and the B & SWU. In 1903 a dispute between the B & SWU and other labor organizations resulted in an angry controversy in which the B & SWU brought strikebreakers from out of town. Critics of the union accused its leaders of moving into the factory owners' camp in order to protect the union stamp and of operating autocratically. On the other hand, union leaders felt that the organization's survival was paramount to local issues of wages and working conditions. These arguments between the national B & SWU and the fragmented local unions in Lynn remained unresolved for many years.

In 1909 discontented Lynn union representatives formed a new organization, the United Shoe Workers union which stood for decentralized control, policies deriving from needs of ordinary workers, and strong assertion of workers' grievances. Both the B & SWU and the USW represented Lynn shoe workers, each in its own way. In the 1930s Lynn workers rallied to support the militant CIO (Congress of Industrial Organizations) against the more conservative American Federation of Labor. As the industrial picture in Lynn's shoe industry changed, organized labor was a presence to be reckoned with. Labor resisted management's efforts to keep wages low and to increase the pace of work, fighting the relentless subordination of human needs to mechanization and working for fairness in the shops, better pay and labor conditions. Unions were important and natural reactions to industrial change. In Lynn they also had important social functions, sponsoring dances, parties, picnics. Several union halls were key gathering places for members, where workers found easy camaraderie and family-like relationships. Arguments over organized labor's role in the decline of Lynn's shoe industry will continue as long as people have memories of Shoe City. People will also remember the spirit of radicalism in Lynn that survived in the working population from the 1830s until the late twentieth century.

Lynn's shoeworking population expanded and changed dramatically as a result of industrial development. In the late nineteenth and early twentieth century, population growth — more than 40,000 between 1890 and 1920 — put great pressure on the housing supply. Thousands of immigrants arrived from upper New England, Canada, Ireland, Italy, Greece, Russia, Poland, Sweden, and elsewhere, looking for places to live. Between 1900 and 1925, 4,251 structures were built for housing in Lynn. Much of this construction took place in the dense residential neighborhoods surrounding the industrial core. On streets formerly characterized by wide spaces between dwellings and ample back yards, vacant land was crowded with new housing. Many courts and terraces were added within residential blocks by the solid massing of multifamily buildings. Thus many newcomers to Lynn could occupy housing within a mile or two of the shoe factories.

A variety of building types were constructed to house Lynn's changing population. First there were older single-family houses divided up into tenements. Then there were single homes which had one or more rooms for renters and boarders. Two-family houses had been built through much of the nineteenth century. Beginning in the 1890s a new type of multifamily dwelling, the three-decker or triple-decker, emerged in Lynn and became a common type of structure. By 1925 it is estimated that 1500 of these three-story buildings had been constructed in Lynn. Ranging somewhat in size and the luxury of their appointments, three-deckers were a compromise between apartments and single houses. Usually free-standing on three or four sides, they were planned to be open to daylight and ventilation, but overcrowding of buildings on the land often reduced these advantages. With each floor occupied by a single family, three-deckers are still characteristic of many Lynn residential streets. The kitchen setting in this exhibition is intended to represent a typical ethnic shoe worker's family kitchen in a three-decker building about 1915.

Other types of multiunit housing in Lynn included apartment houses for small families and lodging houses for single persons. About 200 lodging and boarding houses existed in the city in 1910, most of them within half a mile of Central Square. Boarding and lodging houses often served immigrants who lived with families speaking their native languages. The changes in housing and living patterns among Lynn's shoeworkers represented basic shifts in the techniques and pace of the shoe industry.

Shoe City reached its height of manufacturing and commercial prosperity between 1900 and 1920. In these years central Lynn bustled with activity. Several massive shoe factories constructed during this period changed the industrial landscape. Stores, restaurants, business and professional services existed to respond to nearly every personal and community need. Principal business areas on Market, Summer, and Union Streets functioned all day and often far into the night. Central Square was generally crowded with people and vehicles and trains; its restaurants, shops, and offices gave the appearance of a far bigger city than Lynn then was. By 1915 the city had eight busy theaters offering a range of entertainment from nickelodeon motion pictures to vaudeville performances, stage shows, and concerts. Electric street railways ran from Central Square in all directions, putting Lynn into easy communication with all nearby towns and cities. Resorts such as Nahant and Revere Beach were only short streetcar or train rides away, and more than 200 trains each day ran to Boston.

In 1900 Lynn celebrated its fiftieth anniversary as an incorporated city with a grand three-day public commemoration. One day was devoted to religious observances, one day to activities in the schools, and the third day climaxed with an immense parade that snaked through the city's streets. Lynners were proud of their accomplishments. An enthusiastic booster spirit characterized the city and survived until the Great Depression of the 1930s. Business leaders supported several periodicals promoting the city, they campaigned to attract industry so as to overcome the disadvantages of a one-industry economy, and they worked to make Lynn a major retail center. "Buy in Lynn" was a favorite business slogan of the 1920s. Such urgent commercialism, typical of American cities, could backfire when conditions in Lynn changed, making it less attractive than rival cities elsewhere in the country.

The late nineteenth and early twentieth centuries were times of intense social vitality for Lynn's working people. Between 1880 and 1940 the city was tied together by a complex series of human networks. People supported hundreds of societies, clubs, fraternal orders, and religious organizations. For example, the Grand Army of the Republic, an organization of Union veterans of the Civil War, claimed hundreds of shoe workers as members. The GAR Lynn post was one of the largest and most active in the country. In 1885 and 1886 the post built the Grand Army Hall which remains on Andrew Street in central Lynn. Fraternal orders such as the Elks, Odd Fellows, Knights of Phythias, Improved Order of Red Men, and their various female auxiliaries had many distinct lodges, tribes, or councils.

Other changes complicated the Lynn social scene after 1900, encouraging new growth in the city's human networks. Between 1899 and 1909 the shoe industry added 7,000 people to its working force until in 1909 nearly 18,000 shoe workers crowded into the factories. Many new workers were native born, probably brought in from northern New England. The majority, however, were foreign-born immigrants. Some immigrants settled in Lynn because they already knew the trade of shoemaking and hoped to practice their skills in a new environment. The largest groups of newcomers arrived from Greece, Italy, Poland, Russia, and Sweden, with lesser numbers from several other nations. Characteristically, these groups formed networks of ethnic organizations, adding to societies already established by Irish and French-Canadian residents of Lynn. The earliest ethnic organizations generally centered around religious traditions — churches, sodalities, congregational guilds. In time each church or synagogue tended to foster a varied complex of ceremonial units, social clubs, fraternal and mutual benefit associations. The largest congregations organized schools. Ethnic groups chartered typical secular organizations — Greek coffee houses, French and Polish credit unions, Jewish charitable societies.

Human networks played crucial roles for Lynn's foreign-born people. Most basic to the immigrants' experience were their families. Many single people arrived first, then sent for family members from the old country. Some young shoe workers brought and married sweethearts from their homelands, while others found spouses in Lynn from their national groups. Along with families, language was a basic tie which brought people together. Out of their languages and religious backgrounds grew the other organizations making up Lynn's human networks. Ethnic institutions and societies served a number of functions. They performed familiar ceremonies and observed traditional customs, making their members feel at home in a strange environment. In churches and clubrooms, speakers of a foreign language could find people with whom to socialize on easy terms. Ethnic organizations helped to mediate the transition of non-native people into an alien situation, offering group solidarity yet, over time, slowly opening opportunities for immigrants to participate more fully in American life.

Other human networks grew out of neighborhoods. Lynn had its ethnic neighborhoods — areas usually near churches — where immigrants clustered. The Polish settlement concentrated around St. Michael's parish, the French-Canadian community surrounding St. Jean Baptiste Church, and the Greek settlement near St. George's Church typified such neighborhoods. One district — the Brickyard — represented another set of relationships in which networks tied members of different nationalities into a cohesive working-class neighborhood. Former residents of the Brickyard recall a rich mixture of peoples. In the same block or even the same buildings, families from six or eight separate national origins might live in close proximity. The Summer Street business area included stores and restaurants representing several distinct cultural traditions, all intermingled. People from the Brickyard remember the close relationships and mutual aid among people of different backgrounds. Here was a new kind of network, lively and diverse, almost in the shadows of the great shoe factory buildings.

Amid the prosperity of early twentieth-century Lynn, few shoe workers realized that they were on the verge of another set of major industrial and social changes. Employment figures tell part of the story — in 1920, 13,480 Lynners worked in the shoe industry, while nearly an equal number (12,433) were employed in the manufacture of electrical equipment. In the decade that followed, shoeworkers diminished, electrical workers increased in numbers. These figures signaled an important change in Lynn's industrial climate.

Lynn's electrical industry grew out of shoe manufacturing. In 1883 several Lynn shoe manufacturers attracted a new concern to the city, the Thomson-Houston Electric Company. Ably managed by leading shoe executive, Charles A. Coffin, and building on the inventions of Elihu Thomson, the new company prospered and in 1892 became part of the combined General Electric Company. Led by G. E., Lynn's electrical industry outproduced the city's shoe factories and became the main local economic resource.

What occurred in Lynn happened to many other New England industrial cities in the 1920s and '30s. Attracted by lower costs and higher profits elsewhere, established manufacturers in businesses such as shoes and textiles moved away from the region. Marginal industrialists went out of business entirely. Cities such as Manchester, New Hampshire, and Lowell, Lawrence, and Fall River, Massachusetts, suffered from severe industrial depressions. In Lynn, as early as the 1920s, the city's specialty — women's fashionable shoes — experienced strong competition from foreign makers. Production and employment continued to decline in the Great Depression of the 1930s, until by 1950 only a few shoe factories still remained in Lynn. Yet the city was more fortunate than several other New England communities because the General Electric Company employed many former shoe workers and contributed otherwise to the economy.

Despite the decline of shoe manufacturing, Lynn retains a rich and durable historical legacy from its years as Shoe City. The exhibition, "Life and Times in Shoe City," indicates some of the elements in Lynn's durable past. Of irreplacable significance are the memories carried by the city's people. Some of these fragile memories have been recorded in an oral history program and now serve as components of the exhibition's narrative text. Other memories inspire works of art: the poems of Vincent Ferrini and the urban landscape paintings of Arnold

Trachtman. Other memories celebrate the Brickyard neighborhood and provide subject matter for such local historians as Chick Gecoya.

More substantial traditions survive. Lynn's labor movement is now dominated by the 8000-member local 201 of the International Union of Electrical Workers, a strong voice for labor against management and vigorous defender of worker solidarity, reminiscent of organized labor during the conflicts of the Shoe City era. Other organizations reflecting ethnic Lynn's human networks continue to function. Some societies, such as the Franco-American War Veterans' Club, continue the pattern of group cohesion after more than three-quarters of a century for the French-Canadian community in Lynn. Physical remains of Shoe City's prosperity also survive: the immense factory buildings dating from the climax of shoe production continue to dominate central Lynn. Long scorned and under-used, these silent monuments to the city's industrial past have suddenly attracted attention as strong architectural forms and enduring urban resources. Reminders of Shoe City persist — some fragile and immaterial, others tangible and substantial — helping to give identity to modern Lynn and its people.

Lynn's past may have a future. Several activities, including this exhibition and the programs associated with it, could renew Shoe City's sense of its history. In particular, a program sponsored by the Commonwealth of Massachusetts is likely to spur the local sense of historical awareness. The Commonwealth has designated Lynn as one of six cities to contain an Urban Heritage State Park. Here the State Park will have an outdoor recreation area on the waterfront tied into the old industrial area where an urban history museum, tentatively located in a former shoe factory, is planned. The museum will give special attention to the Shoe City theme, Lynn's shoe industry and its social history. Thus the development of shoe manufacturing will play yet another role in Lynn's changing story in the nineteenth and twentieth centuries.

An Ancient and Honorable Craft

"The Lynn shoemaker was in many respects a fortunately situated man. His labor was light. He was sheltered from the inclemency of the weather, and his light and generally pleasant shop was an attractive place. The peculiar nature of his business requiring of the workman little mental concentration, allowed him to take part in discussions, or fix his attention upon any question that might engage his thoughts. This circumstance made every workshop a school and an incipient debating club."

David N. Johnson, *Sketches of Lynn or the Changes of Fifty Years (Lynn, 1880) p. 3-4*

"The shoemaker's shop cannot boast of a great antiquity. It came into use about the middle of the last century or a little earlier. The size of these shops varied from the "ten-footer" — as one measuring ten feet in length by ten feet in width was called — to those measuring fourteen feet each way. These were regarded as of almost palatial dimensions. The average was nearer twelve by twelve."

Johnson, *Sketches of Lynn*, p. 23

"A stranger who has not been enlightened upon the ways of the place would be astonished at the number of small square erections, like miniature school-houses, standing each as an appendage to a dwelling-house. These are the 'shoe shops,' where the father of the family and his boys work, while the women within are employed in binding and trimming. Thirty or more of these shoe shops may be counted in a walk of half a mile."

Harriet Martineau, *Society in America* (1837)

The Great Revolution

"The Revolution in the shoe business occurred during the ten years end-
ing 1865. From 1855, or a little later, the workmen began to leave the
"little shop" to work in the factories of the manufacturers; and in a few
years vacant shops were seen all over the city, until most of them were
transformed into hen houses or coal pens, or were moved and joined to
some house to make a snug little kitchen."

Johnson, *Sketches of Lynn*, p. 341

*Shoe stitcher at work about 1901, photo-
graph by Frances Benjamin Johnston.
Courtesy of the Library of Congress.*

"The introduction of sewing machines for the stitching and binding of shoes was the result of an absolute necessity. There was a time when women's busy fingers were able to do all that was required of them; but the time came when they could not, and machinery was called in to their aid."

Lynn, *Reporter*, February 28, 1863

*Consolidated hand-method lasting machine
based on the invention of Jan Matzeliger,
early 20th century. Courtesy of United
Shoe Machinery Corp.*

"A man working exclusively at this branch of the craft soon became an expert, even though he knew nothing else of the art of shoemaking. The 'heeling' was afterward subdivided into 'nailing,' 'shaving,' 'blacking,' and 'polishing;' and from this gradually came the minute division which is now the marked feature in this business, distinguishing the new order of things from the old."

Johnson, *Sketches of Lynn*, p. 341

MODEL C
For General Shoe Factory Use

Skiving machine, early 20th century. Courtesy of United Shoe Machinery Corp.

"It will be seen that the chief characteristic of the revolution that has taken place is, that everything is reduced to system. The exactness of scientific measurement is substituted for random guesses. Everything is assorted with especial reference to its fitness for the purpose intended."

Johnson, *Sketches of Lynn,* p. 18

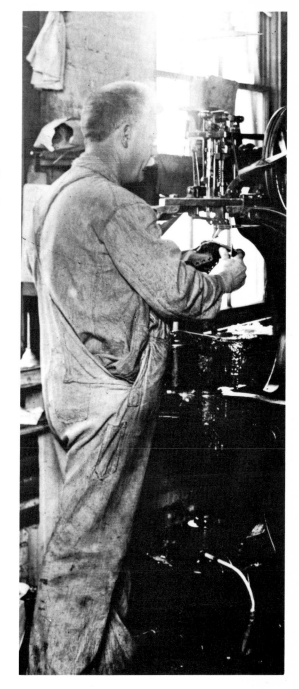

Operative working with a McKay stitcher, early 20th century. Courtesy of Lynn Historical Society.

"Gradually, one after another, machines of various kinds, for 'rolling,' 'stripping,' and 'splitting' leather, and for cutting out soles, have been introduced, effecting more or less change in the method of manufacturing shoes. But the greatest and most important innovation has been the introduction of the new McKay's stitching machine, for uniting the soles and uppers of shoes — a desideratum long sought for, and reached at last. To this machine is to be attributed the great revolution now going on in the shoe manufacture in this city, and which, in all human probability, is to make our city another Lowell or Lawrence, in a different line of business."

Lynn, *Reporter,* February 28, 1863

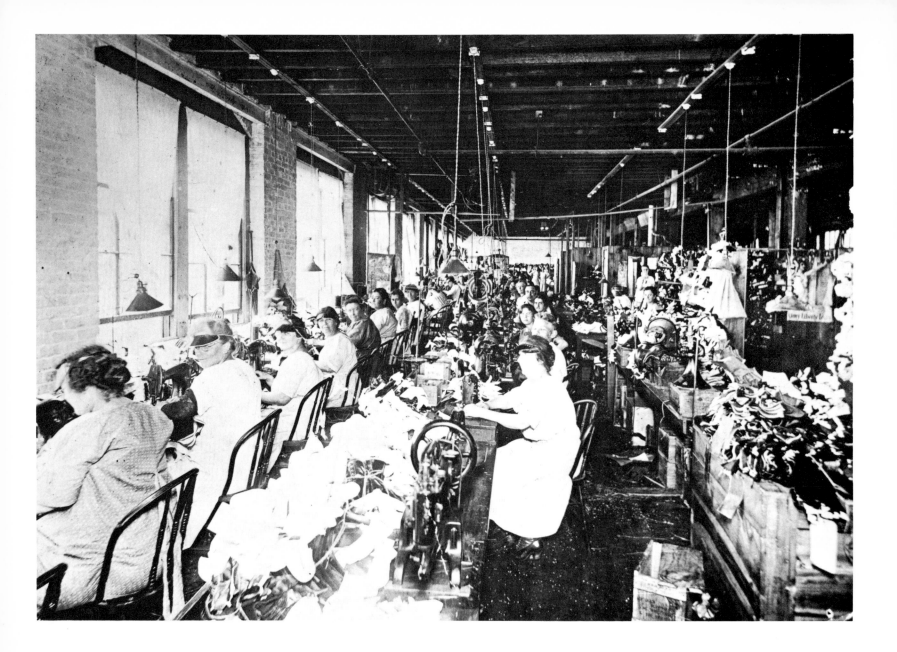

''The rapid progress that has been made, in the introduction of machinery in shoemaking has been beyond all previous calculation. It may almost be said that hand-work has already become the exception, and machinery the rule. The little shoemaker's shop and the shoemaker's bench, are passing rapidly away, soon to be known no more among us, and the immense factory, with its laboring steam engine, and its busy hum of whirling wheels, is rising up in its place to change the whole face of things in this ancient and honored metropolis of the 'workers in the gentle craft of leather.' ''

Lynn, *Reporter,* February 28, 1863

''Mr. Matzeliger was a man of wonderful energy and tenacity of purpose. He started to build his machine with the fixed principle that the one way in which to accomplish the high quality of results obtained by the hand laster was to duplicate his motions and methods. His success is a matter of wonder to those who behold his machine which has triumphed over all changes in style and varying commercial conditions that have come with the passing years.''

Lynn Business Magazine, March, 1902

"That wealth is power is an axiom
the truth of which no man, whose
daily labor earns his daily bread,
will, for a moment, doubt; and experience proves that its possessors
have often used it to oppress and
degrade the laborer. In the present
organization of society the laborer,
single-handed, is powerless, and may
be oppressed with impunity by his
wealthy neighbors; but, acting in
concert with his fellow-laborers,
through a systematic organization,
there is no power of wrong he may
not openly defy."

Journeymen Cordwainers Association Constitution,
Lynn Bay State, March 29, 1860.

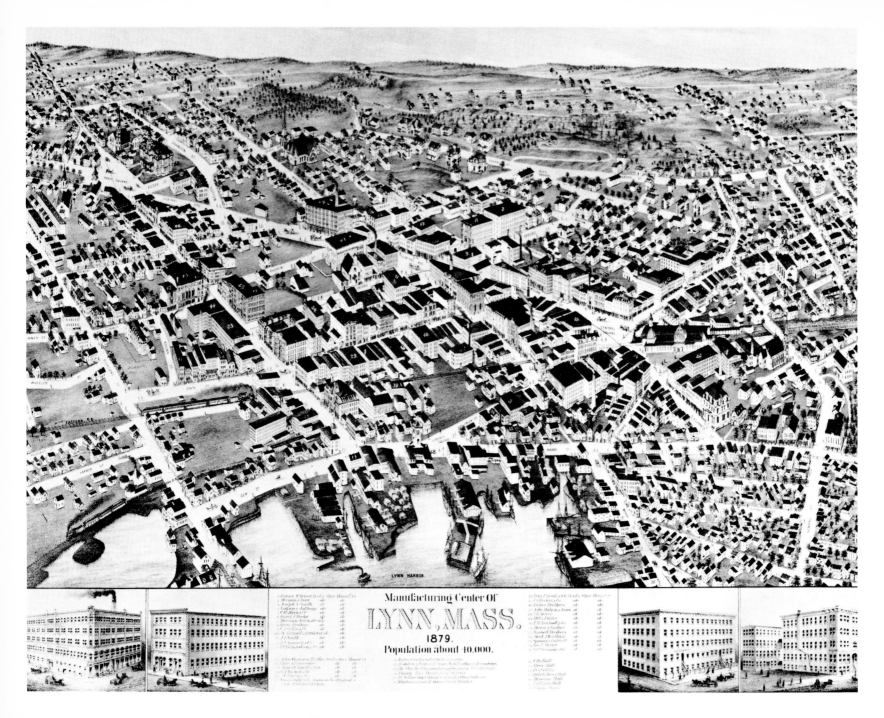

Manufacturing Center Of

LYNN, MASS.

1879.

Population about 40,000.

Entrepreneurs
and Manufacturers

"Of course, the system is yet in its infancy — the business is yet in a transition state; but the wheels of revolution are moving rapidly, and they never turn backward. Operatives are pouring in as fast as room can be made for them, buildings for 'shoe factories' are going up in every direction, the hum of machinery is heard on every hand, old things are passing away, and all things are becoming new."

Lynn, *Reporter*, February 28, 1863

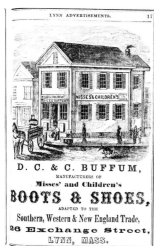

Vamp Building, built in 1903, enlarged in 1907, once the largest shoe factory in the world. Courtesy of Lynn Realty Trust.

"The Vamp Building is a huge building. It takes over a whole block. It takes part of Washington Street, Broad Street, part of Liberty Square and comes around to Union Street and meets Washington Street again. And that's a whole block. It's a huge building of eight stories. And it's shaped like a top of a shoe — the vamp and the two quarters. The whole works. It's shaped like a top of a shoe. And there was many factories in that building. I don't know, four or five shoe factories. Other factories that done business with the shoe factories, like sole cutting factories, inner soles, outer soles, heels, shanks, cement. Small cement factories that manufactured cement or had it brought in, but they sold it to the shoe factories."

Interview with a former shoe worker. Taped interviews from the Lynn Oral History Program, Essex Institute Archives.

Buffum Shoe Factory about 1850. Essex Institute Archives.

"Soon after this the factory system was gradually introduced. One by one the little shoemakers' shops were abandoned, as the factories of the manufacturers were enlarged and fitted up so that the work, both of the stitchers and makers, might be done under the more immediate supervision of the employers."

Johnson, *Sketches of Lynn*, p. 16

Shoe factory environment about 1901, photograph by Frances Benjamin Johnston. Courtesy of the Library of Congress.

"The arrangements of this building are perfect in their way. It is a complete beehive of industry; everything is systematized, everything economized, and each part made to act in concert with every other part. There is no clashing or jarring, and the harmony that prevails speaks volumes for the master mind that planned and controls its operations. There is no attempt at ornament or display about this establishment, but everything is substantial, and eminently adapted to the use for which it is designed. It may be justly regarded as one of the pioneers in the new crusade of machinery in behalf of muscle, and if it is an experiment at all, it is a most perfect and successful one."

Lynn, *Reporter*, February 28, 1863

"He [Philip A. Chase] was a pioneer in the introduction of shoe machinery, being for some devices the first, and for others the second or third to use them in this city. . . . He realized that more men are ruined by bad book-keeping than by bad debts, and accurate methods of cost keeping were kept well in hand, the raw material was bought shrewdly and the goods sold cautiously. . . . With years of profits and of prudence, surplus funds were kept in available form and the nimble penny had its run ahead of the slow shilling."

Lynn Historical Society, *Register,* 1903, pp. 56-57.

Oxford Club headquarters opened in 1892. Essex Institute Archives.

Factory and home of Samuel M. Bubier at Market and Oxford Streets, late 1860's. Courtesy of Frederick H. Bubier.

"Club life in Lynn has marked the beginning of a distinct epoch in its history this week by opening to the public of a building devoted exclusively to social purposes. The Oxford Club's new house on Washington square was thrown open Wednesday evening . . . .The whole structure is probably the best of the kind to be found in New England, outside of Boston, and reflects great credit upon all who were in any way connected with its production."

Lynn Scrapbooks, volume 28
Lynn Public Library

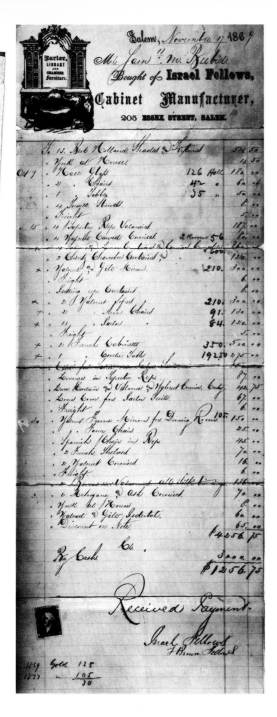

''Our friend [Samuel M. Bubier] who has just been taken from us was a strong man. With no special advantages to start with, he became a power in business circles. He was elevated to the highest office in the gift of his townsmen. His name will be associated with blocks of substantial buildings while brick and stone shall endure. It will be connected with municipal enactments while the records of the city shall exist.''

Lynn Item, October 20, 1894

''Machinery creates wealth; and a large part of the increase naturally falls into the hands of capital that employs the machinery. Colossal fortunes are piled up in a few years, apparently making wider the gap between rich and poor.''

Lynn, *Transcript,* December 20, 1879

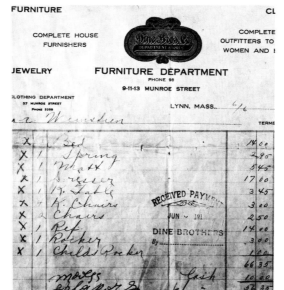

''Those who look beneath the surface of things, with unprejudiced eyes, are painfully conscious that wealth, though year by year on the increase, goes now into fewer hands; that the results of industry are very unequally divided; that the advantages which machinery and labor bring, have been altogether in favor of capital and against labor, and these evils are dangerously increasing from year to year.''

Massachusetts Bureau of Labor, *Fourth Annual Report,* 1873, p. 306

A Community of Workers

"I was fourteen then and after graduation you hot-footed right down to City Hall and got your card and went to work. Practically all kids in those days went to work at fourteen. They had to in order to take the load off their parents, sort of to help, to help things along. And they'd work at anything, it didn't matter what it was."

Interview with a former shoe worker

"I'm strong for unions. I believe labor must have a union. In the shoe factory, if there wasn't a union everyone would have been walking out of there with 50 cents a day. Even today if the people who run the management could do it, they would not pay anything. That's why we had to have a union."

Interview with a former shoe worker

NOTICE

TO ALL WHOM IT MAY CONCERN:

The Albert Getz Shoe Manufacturing Company, an Ohio corporation, having its works, its principal office and doing business at Lancaster, Ohio, contracts with its employes with the express understanding that each person employed by it is not a member of the Boot and Shoe Workers' Union nor a member of the United Shoe Workers of America; that such person will not become a member of the Boot and Shoe Workers' Union nor become a member of the United Shoe Workers of America while an employe of The Albert Getz Shoe Manufacturing Company; that The Albert Getz Shoe Manufacturing Company is run non-union and agrees with such person that it will run non-union while such person is in its employ; that if at any time while employed by The Albert Getz Shoe Manufacturing Company such person wants to become connected with the Boot and Shoe Workers' Union or any affiliated organization, or wants to become connected with the United Shoe Workers of America or any affiliated organization, such person agrees to withdraw from the employment of The Albert Getz Shoe Manufacturing Company; and that while an employe of The Albert Getz Shoe Manufacturing Company such person will not make any effort amongst its employes to bring about the unionizing of that Company's shoe manufacturing plant against that Company's wish.

THE ALBERT GETZ SHOE MANUFACTURING COMPANY.

"Yellow Dog" anti-union broadside, early 20th century. Courtesy of Boot and Shoe Workers Union.

''I'll tell you I always belonged to the union. I believed with the union but at one time the union was too strong. There were three different unions in the city of Lynn, and they didn't agree. They were fighting between each about who was going to control, that's how we lost quite a lot of factories in the city of Lynn because of the union.''

Interview with a former shoe worker

Daily Evening Item. **EXTRA**

If You Have TENEMENTS TO LET, HOUSES FOR SALE.

VOL. LI. NO. 39   LYNN, MASS, THURSDAY JANUARY 22, 1903.   PRICE TWO CENTS.

QUIET IS ONCE MORE RESTORED IN THE CITY.

Boot and Shoe Workers' Union Cutters Went to Work This Morning, Some of Them Without Police Escort, and There Was No Sign of Disturbance.

C. J. M'MORROW HAS ARRIVED IN LYNN

President Tobin Calls General Organizer From Chicago to Assist in Lynn Contest—Union Stamp Shoe Manufacturers Vote to Employ None But B. & S. W. U. Workmen—Mayor Eastham's Energetic Action Resulted in Good Order Wednesday Evening—The Police Had Orders to Use Clubs if Needed—Crowds in Streets Restrained From Serious Outbreak—Marshal Burckes Made One Arrest—Injunction Hearing Against K. of L. Cutters' Officers in Boston To-day.

SPLENDID WORK OF LYNN POLICE AT WASHINGTON STREET RAILROAD CROSSING

The cutters, under escort, are seen across the street, while the police are threatening the mob with their clubs and keeping the crossing clear for the approaching train.

''The unions had a lot of members there. About ten thousand members. It was very strong unions, but it was strikes all the time. Every week, here and there, they would go out in the streets and picket the places. They won every strike, but the factories gone and out of business. They were pretty strong, these unions.''

Interview with a former shoe worker

"The frequency with which the eye meets the sign 'Rooms to let' convinces a visitor that the population of Lynn must be in a state of constant coming and going. Those who come are more than those go."

The Boot and Shoe Industry in Massachusetts as a Vocation for Women,
U.S. Department of Labor, 1915, p. 17

"More than $2,000,000 worth of additional city valuation is represented in the new buildings which are now under construction in Lynn, and indications point toward the establishment of a record, especially for large apartment houses and factory construction."

Board of Trade Journal, 1912, p. 11

Wedding of Harold and Nellie Day,
October 12, 1914, at 28 Flint Street,
Lynn. Courtesy of Gertrude D. Connolly.

''I don't say we celebrated Sunday, but my mother didn't work on Sundays. She tried to have her roast cooked on Saturday, her dessert cooked on Saturday. She worked hard. She baked beans, she baked bread, and made her pudding for Sunday. She always had a day for each thing, and you couldn't get away from that day. She was terrible. Her daughters, none of them are like that. My mother, she said 'if I didn't have a routine, I wouldn't get things done.' Sunday night we took the laundry down, off of Broadway. An Italian lady did it, she did it by hand too, and dried it. And we'd bring it back on Monday and my mother would sprinkle it and Tuesday she would have to iron it. That was the day when things had to be starched. We wore these petticoats with ruffles and tucks and lace and everything. She had to do that that certain day. And she would also cook on Tuesdays. She always made three pies on Tuesdays, three pies on Fridays. She used to fry donuts, make bread and she really cooked.''

Interview with a Lynn resident.

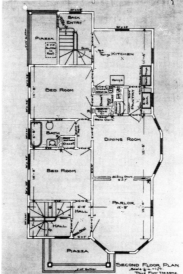

Floor plan of a Lynn three-decker house, early 20th century. Courtesy of Buildings Department, Lynn City Hall.

''It was a small house with, what I would call, double parlors. A large doorway separating the two parlors and then there was a dining room and a kitchen. And then upstairs, 1,2,3 bedrooms and a lovely attic of which part was finished and one room not finished. After my father died, my mother had roomers. So she and I slept in the attic bedroom and my uncle lived with us and he slept in the room downstairs at the back of the house. So that meant that there were two quite large bedrooms rented.''

Interview with a Lynn resident.

Shoe City

"You bring your dinner, or you go down the square to eat. There were more people going out to eat in Central Square in Lynn than any place in Boston during a busy time. There were twenty places to eat along Central Square. There were plenty of us there, plenty of people there at noontime. It was good, it was a busy place, Lynn, it was one of the busiest places there was on the North Shore."

Interview with a former shoe worker

40

Young woman at Lynn beach, early 20th century. Courtesy of Robert Marcotte.

Central Square Theater, about 1911, built for vaudeville performances. Essex Institute Archives.

"It seemed to be a city of prosperity. I mean we had lots of theaters; there was lots of activity downtown on Saturdays. They had a vaudeville theater, at the Olympia Theater. We had the Strand Theater, the Capitol Theater, the Waldorf, the Paramount, the auditorium, which had stage productions."

Interview with a former shoe worker

"Lynn Beach, which connects the Nahants to the main land, is two miles in length on the eastern side, and two and a half miles on the western. It is an isthmus, or causeway, of fine, shining gray sand, forming a curve, and rising so high in the centre as generally to prevent the tide from passing over."

Alonzo Lewis and James R. Newhall, *History of Lynn . . .* (Lynn: 1890) p. 66

Huntt's Restaurant, a favorite haunt of shoe workers in Central Square, about 1911. Essex Institute Archives.

Lynn's lodging house district, Blake and Mulberry Streets, about 1911. Essex Institute Archives.

"The only special restaurant that I remember was the Huntt's Restaurant on Central Square. It was one of the biggest restaurants we had in the city, and most everyone used to go in there. Even at noon time you'd go there to eat, nighttimes, Saturdays, Sundays, the place would be filled with people eatin' mostly all shoe workers talkin' about shoes and the jobs."

Interview with a former shoe worker

"In nearly every quarter of Lynn the lodging house is prominent, but near the railroad station and the larger factories the 'Rooms to let' sign is seen in most of the houses. The prices for rooms are uniformly high, though the conditions vary greatly. A large four story lodging house near the civic center contains 143 rooms let by day, week, or month. The majority of these rooms are of fair size, some have good light and air, but the furniture is shabby, and both rooms and furnishing sorely need cleaning."

The Boot and Shoe Industry in Massachusetts as a Vocation for Women, p. 23

F. W. Woolworth Store, Market Street, about 1911. Essex Institute Archives.

Summer Street, one of Lynn's busiest neighborhood commercial districts, Essex Institute Archives.

''You couldn't walk down Broad Street, Washington Street, Union Street, all you could hear was machines humming, people working. At five o'clock when they'd come out of work, why the sidewalks would be crowded with people going home, stopping at the restaurants or diners and having something to eat or having a drink or whatever.''

Interview with a former shoe worker

''Summer Street was the heart of the city of Lynn, Summer and Market Street. Why the stores would stay open till 9, 9:30, 10 o'clock nights. People there was. The stores were busy, there was hundreds of stores, all kinds from restaurants to clothing stores, baker shops, fruit stands, from one end of Summer Street to the other.''

Interview with a former shoe worker

"Lynn had the best shoemakers in the world, best shoe workers any-where in the world. Just think, there were over a hundred shoe manufac-turers in the city of Lynn, all *fine upstanding* people."

Interview with a former office worker in a shoe factory

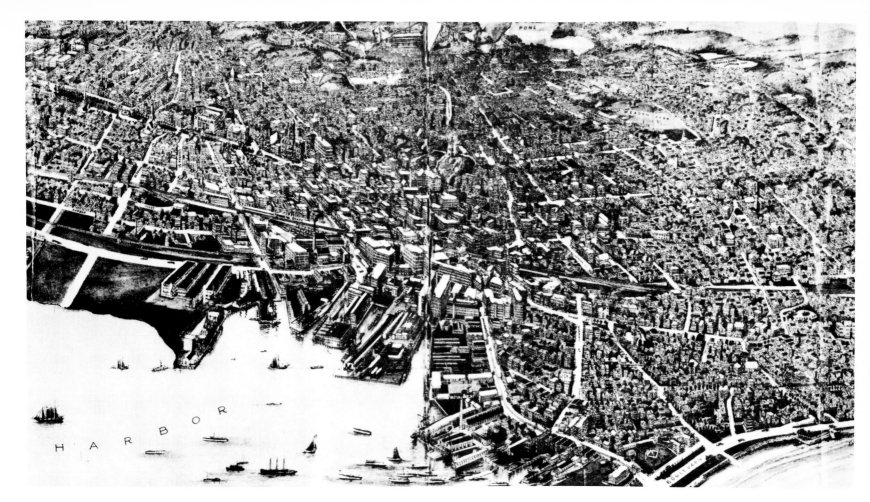

*Aero view of Lynn, 1916, advertising the city
in most enthusiastic terms. Courtesy of Cecil Weinstein.*

" 'Two hundred thousand in 1920,' is the slogan of Lynn, the shoe center
and ideal home city of the country. The city is about to enter upon an era
of industrial, commercial and civic prosperity, in such fashion and with
such speed that every community in this section as well as other sections
of the country, will realize that Lynn is the best city in the United States.
The citizens have spoken and are backing up their slogan with hard and
energetic work, besides the necessary funds and enthusiasm."

Lynn Chamber of Commerce
Journal, November, 1913

"I'm glad I came to America. In a way I'm glad, yes. Very glad because
if I was in Greece I was going to be in war like my brother who was in
war twenty years straight. I'm glad I got away from that. I had tough
times, but since I retired I have had all good times."

Interview with a former shoe worker

Human Networks

St. Michael's Polish Roman Catholic
Church, Summer Street, about 1910.
Essex Institute Archives.

"St. Michael the Archangel is invoked as the protector of Christians in the battle against the powers of hell and as a helper in all the dangers of salvation. . . . Was it not fitting, therefore, that in 1903 a group of political and economic refugees from Poland gathered together under his protection and guardianship. Was it not most fitting to dedicate the new Church to his honor. These pioneers stood in need of St. Michael's help to remain steadfast in the Faith, while their way of life was being violently changed by an industrial revolution."

St. Michael's Parish, Lynn
50 Golden Years, 1906-1956

Scandinavian Evangelical Church, Johnson Street, early 20th century. Essex Institute Archives.

"Somebody told me when I came to Lynn. I asked them, 'Can you tell me where I can see a shoe factory?' So he said, 'Oh, I can hear, you are a Swede. There's a Swedish shoe factory over on the corner. Go in there.' I got a job."

Interview with a former shoe worker

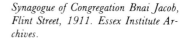
Synagogue of Congregation Bnai Jacob, Flint Street, 1911. Essex Institute Archives.

"Well, they did make bricks there but back before my time. I guess that's why they call it a brick yard. But it was a rough neighborhood. When I mean rough I mean the boys. If eight or ten of them got together and walked downtown, and they knew you was from the brick yard they moved quick, when they saw you coming. They were rough and tough. A lot of Irishmen down there, a lot of Italians and a few Greeks . . . and Jewish. Back in the twenties. Of course we all lived together like neighbors, probably in the same building. You know, I'd live on the first floor, a Jewish family would be on the second floor. There was no discrimination or anything of the kind. We all lived together, played together, fought together at times."

Interview with a former shoe worker

*St. Jean's School, 9th grade, 1921.
Parochial schools such as this one were key
elements in Lynn's ethnic communities.
Courtesy of Donna Landry.*

*Picnic of the LaFrance Mutual Aid Socie-
ty, 1915. Courtesy of United Shoe
Workers, Local 2.*

*St. Jean Baptiste French parochial school,
Endicott Street, constructed in 1899. Essex
Institute Archives.*

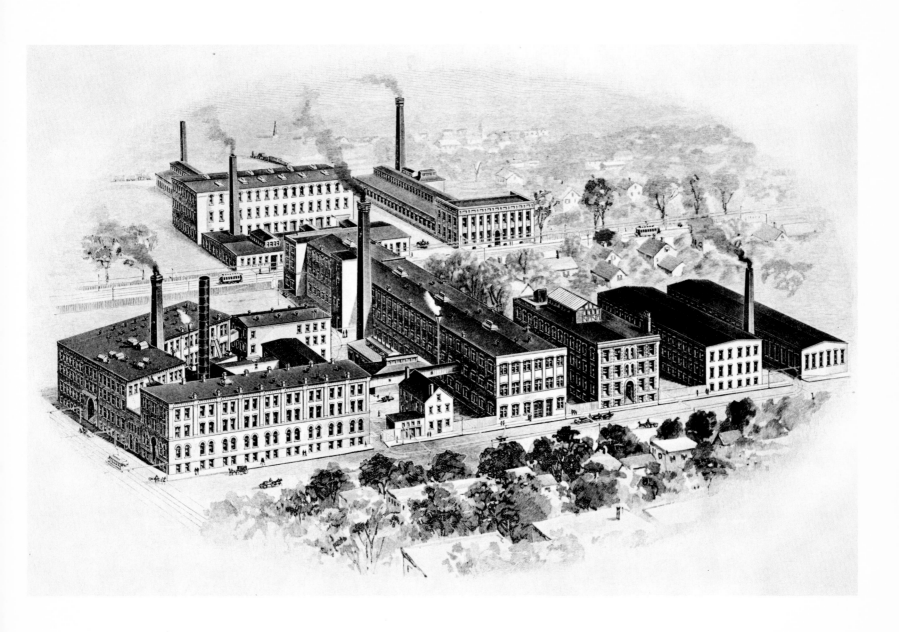

A Durable Past

''The Company's Factory for the manufacture of electrical machinery is the largest and best equipped in the world, and we are the only Electric Company prepared to furnish our customers with systems of both Arc and Incandescent Lighting, Motors for the Electrical Transmission of Power, and a complete improved system of Electric Tramways.''

Thompson-Houston Electric Company, General Catalogue,
December 1, 1890

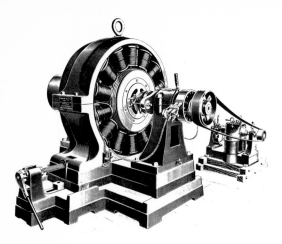

Products of the Thomson-Houston Electric Co. Its specialties included arc light systems and dynamos. Essex Institute Archives.

"There is little need of calling particular attention to the merits of the Thomson-Houston apparatus. The marvelous increase in the Company's business during the past few years is the best indication that it has the most complete and economical system of Electric Lighting and Power Transmission before the public today."

Thompson-Houston Electric Company,
General Catalogue, December 1, 1890

View of Lynn, painting by Arnold Trachtman. Courtesy of the Artist.

THE CITY

by Vincent Ferrini
Courtesy of the Author

15 years ago this city was the shoe hub of the world.
160 factories hummed a song of joy.
Jobs were so plentiful you tripped over them.
And our families had happiness.
Today the city is a graveyard of factories
Monumental tombstones accusing with broken eyes.
A jungle of death pregnant with another life.
And we shoeworkers
Idly mushroom the union halls arguing.
Skeptical of the future, we talk of the past:
Of the crowded union meetings,
The honest speeches inspiring guts to sacrifice,
The monster demonstrations and the unbreakable strikes.
6 months ago the last giant factory
Said 'Accept a 20% cut.'
The Union answered 'NO!'
The Boss grabbed his shop and settled out of the state
Leaving 1700 families stranded.
The Union caved in.
At dawn busses and cars carry shoeworkers
     to far-away open shop towns.
And we thousands remaining
Huddled in tenements
Starve in the shadows of dead factories.

"A final role of Heritage State Parks may be simply described as restoring a public sense of the importance and viability of our urban centers. The decline of our cities has been marked by a wide-spread notion that older downtown and industrial areas are unattractive, dangerous, and to be avoided, or part of a past that deserves to be forgotten. These parks will show that these areas were keystones of the Commonwealth's economic and social development and were of national or even worldwide importance. Further, they will show the ways in which the people who lived and worked in the cities contributed to their rise and significance. Finally, they will highlight the present-day economic and cultural value of the resouces that remain from these times."

Urban Heritage State Parks, pamphlet issued by the Massachusetts Department of Environmental Management

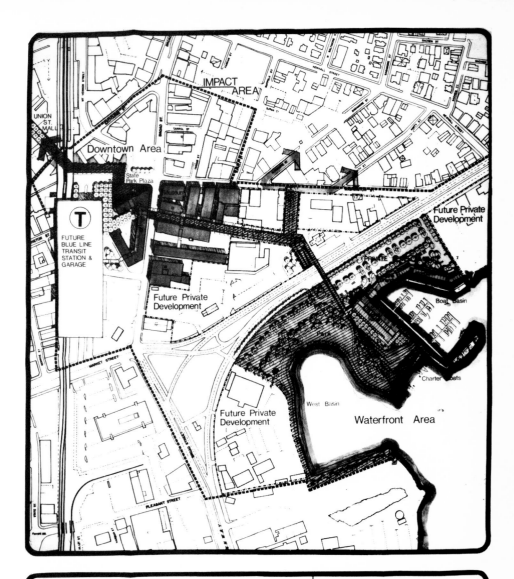

IMPACT AREA

UNION ST. MALL

Downtown Area

State Park Plaza

T

FUTURE BLUE LINE TRANSIT STATION & GARAGE

Future Private Development

Future Private Development

PRIVATE

Future Private Development

Boat Basin

Charter Boats

West Basin

Waterfront Area

MARKET STREET

PLEASANT STREET

Downtown/Waterfront Revitalization Project

CITY OF LYNN, MASSACHUSETTS

Lynn Heritage State Park

Date October 2, 1978	Exhibit No.
Sasaki Associates, Inc.	
CONCEPTUAL LAND USE PLAN	

0 100 200 300 400
Scale in feet

N